GRADE 2

Treasures

D1369717

English Language Learner Practice Book

Macmillan/McGraw-Hill

How to Use this Book

Based on the needs of your English Language Learners, you may need to accommodate how to use this book with your students.

- Read the directions with students and review any visuals or labels on the page.

- Work through the examples with students as a group, modeling how to fill in the pages.

- Have students work in pairs, pairing more proficient English speakers with less proficient English speakers.

At the bottom of each page, additional suggestions are provided to address the English Language Learners at the Beginning/Intermediate levels.

B

The McGraw·Hill Companies

 Macmillan/McGraw-Hill

Published by Macmillan/McGraw-Hill, of McGraw-Hill Education, a division of The McGraw-Hill Companies, Inc., Two Penn Plaza, New York, New York 10121.

ed in the United States of America

6 7 8 9 WDQ 14 13 12 11 10

Contents

Name _____

Phonics/Word Study: Short *a, i*
Circle the word with the short *a* sound.

1.

cat

cow

2.

bowl

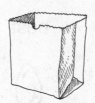

bag

Circle the word with the short *i* sound. Say the word.

3.

pig

pan

4.

ring

cat

Beginning/Intermediate Review how to decode. Point to and name the pictures. Point out your mouth position. Have children repeat and practice saying the words with a partner. Have them listen to the **Sound Pronunciation CD**.

Name _____

Phonics: Consonant Blends

Circle the consonant blend *sl*, *sp*, *sk*, or *st* in each word.

1.

nest

2.

skating

3.

spoon

4.

slide

Circle the word with the consonant blend. Then write the word on the line. Say the word.

5. slip   kite   hit   _____

6. bee   stem   eat   _____

7. skate   bat   bean   _____

Read the Decodable Reader *Pat and Tim* with a partner.

Beginning/Intermediate Read and point to examples 1–4. Have partners complete all the examples and say words 5–8 to each other. Children can listen to the **Sound Pronunciation CD**.

Name _____

Use the word chart to study this week's vocabulary words.
Write a sentence using each word in your writer's notebook.

Word	Context Sentence	Illustration
groan _____	Sam let out a <u>groan</u> when he spilled his milk.	
excited _____	I like school and am <u>excited</u> to be here.	**Describe how you feel when you are excited.**
whisper _____	I <u>whisper</u> a secret to my friend.	
carefully _____	I gave him the glass <u>carefully</u> so the juice would not spill.	**What do you do carefully?**
different _____	I am wearing two <u>different</u> shoes!	

© Macmillan/McGraw-Hill

Beginning/Intermediate Review vocabulary. Use gestures to demonstrate meaning. Pair children to write one or two sentences, or draw pictures, to illustrate the meaning of the newly acquired vocabulary.

Name _____

Grammar: Statements and Questions
Read the sentences below. Circle each question.
Underline each statement.

1. The rain comes down.

2. Who will go out in the rain?

3. Ann will go out.

4. What will Ann do in the rain?

Read the sentences. Circle the sentence that is
written correctly.

5. Ann plays in the puddles.

   Ann plays in the puddles

6. does she like to splash

   Does she like to splash?

7. Can Ann stay dry?

   can Ann stay dry

8. no, Ann will get wet

   No, Ann will get wet.

Beginning/Intermediate Read the directions for each section and
model the first example. Have children work with partners to complete
examples and say sentences to each other.

Name _____

Read each question and prompt. Discuss the answers with your group. Use *David's New Friends* to find details to support your answers. Then write your answers on the blank lines or on another sheet of paper.

1. Describe the classroom in the story.

   _____

2. Tell about the teacher in the story you read.

   _____

3. What happened to the lizard?

   _____

4. Talk about how people help one another in the story.

   _____

5. What surprised you in the story you read?

   _____

6. Write one question about *David's New Friends* to ask your group.

   _____

   _____

Beginning/Intermediate Read the directions. Pair children to answer the questions using basic and content vocabulary. Have them share their answers with the group. If needed, listen to the selection on **StudentsWork Plus Online**.

Grade 2 Unit I Week I 5

Name _____

Phonics/Word Study: Short *e, o, u*
Circle the word that names each picture.

1.    shell   ship

2.    sand   sun

3.    man   mop

Fill in the blank to complete each word. Say the word.

4.    l _____ g

5.    f _____ x

6.    p _____ p

Beginning/Intermediate Review how to decode. Point to and name the pictures. Point out your mouth position. Have children repeat and practice saying the words with a partner. Have them listen to the **Sound Pronunciation CD**.

Name _____

Phonics: Consonant Digraphs

Circle the word with the consonant digraph *ch* or *th* in each row. Then write the word on the line. Say the word.

1.	three	team	ten	_____
2.	can	cook	cheer	_____
3.	tear	ton	thank	_____
4.	lucky	lunch	learn	_____
5.	chore	cane	cougar	_____
6.	earn	earth	wing	_____

Sight Words

Circle the word you hear. Write the word.

7.	the	to	said	_____
8.	some	could	little	_____
9.	you	was	are	_____
10.	do	they	of	_____

Read the Decodable Reader *Len and Gus* with a partner. Find the words *do, are, said, some*.

Beginning/Intermediate 1-6: Model example 1 and say the words for children to repeat. 7-10: Ask children to repeat the word you say before they circle and write the word.

Name _____

Use the word chart to study this week's vocabulary words. Write a sentence using each word in your writer's notebook.

Word	Context Sentence	Illustration
share _____	We can <u>share</u> the ice cream.	
enjoyed _____	We <u>enjoyed</u> the ice cream.	
wonderful _____	The ice cream tastes <u>wonderful</u>.	**What food tastes wonderful to you?**
thinning _____	The crowd is <u>thinning</u> out as people leave the game.	
delighted _____	I am <u>delighted</u> to see you!	
company _____	My cat keeps me <u>company</u> at night.	

Beginning/Intermediate Review vocabulary. Use gestures to demonstrate meaning. Pair children to write sentences, or draw pictures, to illustrate the meaning of the newly acquired vocabulary and tell sentences to each other.

Grammar: Commands and Exclamations

Read each sentence. Circle the word that tells if the sentence is an exclamation or a command.

1. You scored a goal!

   command   exclamation

2. Pass me a pencil.

   command   exclamation

3. Do not go to bed late.

   command   exclamation

4. We had a great day!

   command   exclamation

Write an exclamation point (!) on the line if the sentence is an exclamation. Write a period (.) if the sentence is a command.

5. We won _____

6. There is the ball _____

7. Please share your toys _____

Beginning/Intermediate Read the directions for each section and model the first example. Point out the exclamation point. Have children work with partners to complete examples and say sentences to each other.

Grade 2 Unit 1 Week 2 9

© Macmillan/McGraw-Hill

Read each question and prompt. Discuss the answers with your group. Use *Mr. Putter and Tabby Pour the Tea* to find details to support your answers. Then write your answers on the blank lines or on another sheet of paper.

1. Describe the things Mr. Putter liked to do.

_____

2. What was Mr Putter's problem?

_____

3. What did Mr. Putter do to solve his problem?

_____

4. List some things Mr. Putty and Tabby did together.

_____

5. How did the story end?

_____

6. Write one question about *Mr. Putter and Tabby Pour the Tea* to ask your group.

_____

_____

Beginning/Intermediate Read the directions. Pair children to answer the questions using basic and content vocabulary. Have them share answers with the group. If needed, they can listen to the selection on **StudentsWork Plus Online**.

Name_____

Phonics/Word Study: Short *a* and Long *a* (*a – e*)
Circle the word with the short *a* sound.

1.

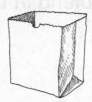 

bag   book

2.

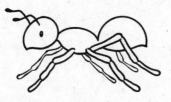 

ant   bowl

3.

 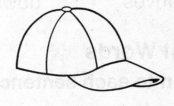

cow   cap

Circle the word with the long *a* sound.
Then write the word on the line. Say the word.

4. cake   cook   cure   _____

5. skin   skate   shoe   _____

6. run   rod   rake   _____

7. sleep   snow   snake   _____

Beginning/Intermediate Review how to decode. Point to and name the pictures.
Point out your mouth position. Have children repeat and practice saying the words
with a partner. Have them listen to the **Sound Pronunciation CD**.   **Grade 2 Unit 1 Week 3** 11

Phonics: Consonant Blends *sl, dr, sk, sp, st*

Circle the word that completes each sentence. Write the word on the line. Then circle the consonant blend in the word.

1. Peg likes many _____.

   sports   slim

2. She likes to _____.

   drove   skate

3. She has fun on _____.

   skis   spoon

4. Today her family _____ to the hills.

   drives   down

Sight Words

Listen to each sentence that is read. Write the word that is missing.

done	another	put	they

5. Tim _____ his sled in the car.

6. He is _____ sledding.

7. His sister will pick _____ sport.

8. _____ will play.

Read the Decodable Reader *You Can Bake a Cake!* **with a partner. Find the words** *put, another, some, done.*

Beginning/Intermediate 1-4: Say the words for each sound. Have children repeat. Ask partners to read the sentences. 5-8: Ask children to repeat the completed sentence after you, before writing the missing word.

Name _____

Use the word chart to study this week's vocabulary words. Write a sentence using each word in your writer's notebook.

Word	Context Sentence	Illustration
harvest _____	The apples are red and ready to <u>harvest</u>.	
crops _____	Some farmers sell their <u>crops</u> at the market.	**What other <u>crops</u> might you find at the market?**
regrow _____	We <u>regrow</u> the same plants in our garden every year.	
machines _____	Some families have these <u>machines</u> in the basement.	**What are these <u>machines</u> used for?**
irrigate _____	Pipes bring water to <u>irrigate</u> the field.	

© Macmillan/McGraw-Hill

Beginning/Intermediate Review vocabulary. Use gestures to demonstrate meaning. Pair children to write sentences, or draw pictures, to illustrate the meaning of the newly acquired vocabulary and tell sentences to each other.

Name _____

Grammar: Subjects

Circle the subject in each sentence.

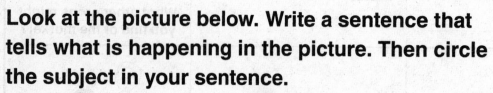

1. An alarm rings.

2. Firefighters jump into the fire truck.

3. You tell the person about the fire.

4. Smoke can hurt you.

5. People call 911 for help.

Look at the picture below. Write a sentence that tells what is happening in the picture. Then circle the subject in your sentence.

_____

_____

Beginning/Intermediate Read each set of directions and model the first example. Have partners circle the subjects and write sentences. Have children share their sentences with the group.

Name_____

Read each question and prompt. Discuss the answers with your group. Use *Family Farm: Then and Now* to find details to support your answers. Then write your answers on the blank lines or on another sheet of paper.

1. What was farming like in North America in old times?

_____

2. How did farming change when Europeans came to North America?

_____

3. Tell how families ran farms in the past.

_____

4. What has happened to family farms today?

_____

5. What is the main thing you learned about farms in North America?

_____

6. Write a question about *Family Farm: Then and Now* to ask your group.

_____

_____

© Macmillan/McGraw-Hill

Beginning/Intermediate Read the directions. Pair children to answer the questions using basic and content vocabulary. Have them share answers with the group. If needed, they can listen to the selection on **StudentsWork Plus Online**.

Phonics/Word Study: Long *i* (*i – e*) and Short *i*
Write the word that names the picture on the line.

1.

_____

2.

_____

3.

_____

4.

_____

Underline the word with the short *i* sound. Say the word.

5. fish   fun   find

6. pen   pin   pine

7. door   do   dish

Beginning/Intermediate Review how to decode words. In each section, read and point to one word with the new sound. Point out your mouth position. Have children say the words. Children can listen to the **Sound Pronunciation CD**.

Name_____

Phonics: Soft *c* and *g*

got	guess	city	cell
gentle	face	car	gerbil
cent	germ	cage	good

**Read each word in the box. Listen for soft *c* and soft *g*.
Write the word in the correct box below.**

Soft *c*	Soft *g*
1.	5.
2.	6.
3.	7.
4.	8.

**Choose words from the soft *c* or soft *g* list to complete
each sentence. Write the word on the line.**

9. Ken has a big smile on his _____.

10. He just got a pet _____.

11. He keeps his pet in a _____.

12. His new pet is very _____.

Read the Decodable Reader *Mike's Big Bike* with a partner.

Beginning/Intermediate Read each set of directions. Model examples 1 and 5.
Say each word for children to repeat. Have partners complete the examples and
say the words. Children can listen to the **Sound Pronunciation CD**.

Name _____

Use the word chart to study this week's vocabulary words. Write a sentence using each word in your writer's notebook.

Word	Context Sentence	Illustration
cultures _____	These people come from many <u>cultures</u>.	**What culture do you come from?**
deaf _____	She cannot hear because she is <u>deaf</u>.	
signing _____	She is <u>signing</u> the words "I love you."	
relatives _____	My aunt and other <u>relatives</u> came for dinner.	
celebrate _____	They came to <u>celebrate</u> my birthday.	**How do you celebrate a special time?**

Beginning/Intermediate Review vocabulary. Use gestures to demonstrate meaning. Pair children to write sentences, or draw pictures, to illustrate the meaning of the newly acquired vocabulary and tell sentences to each other.

Name_____

Grammar: Predicates

Underline the predicate of each sentence.

1. Guide dogs are special dogs.

2. Guide dogs help blind people.

3. The dogs go to guide dog school.

4. Guide dogs learn hand signals.

Write a sentence about the picture.
Then circle the predicate in your sentence.

5.

_____

6.

_____

Beginning/Intermediate Read the directions for each section and
model the first example. Have children work with partners to complete
examples. Have them share their sentences with the group.

Read each question and prompt. Discuss the answers with your group. Use *Meet Rosina* to find details to support your answers. Then write your answers on the blank lines or on another sheet of paper.

1. What is Rosina's special skill?

   _____

2. How does Rosina talk?

   _____

3. Explain how Rosina's day is different from your day.

   _____

4. List three things that Rosina does during a day that you do as well.

   _____

5. What is the name of the book that Rosina and her friends wrote? What is the book about?

   _____

6. Write one question about *Meet Rosina* to ask your group.

   _____

   _____

© Macmillan/McGraw-Hill

Beginning/Intermediate Read the directions. Pair children to answer the questions using basic and content vocabulary. Have them share answers with the group. If needed, they can listen to the selection on **StudentWorks Plus**.

Name_____

Phonics/Word Study: Short *o, u* and Long *o(o – e), u(u – e)*

Circle the word with the short *o* or short *u* sound.

1.

         rope   knot

2.

         goat   fox

3.

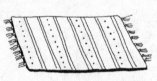   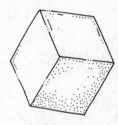

        rug   cube

Circle the word with the long *o* or long *u* sound. Then write the word on the line. Say the word.

4. nose   nine   new   _____

5. sock   stone   sea   _____

6. mud   mat   mule   _____

7. cute   comb   cub   _____

Beginning/Intermediate Read and point to the words in examples 1–3 to give examples of the four new sounds. Point out your mouth position. Have children say the words with a partner. Children can listen to the **Sound Pronunciation CD.**

Name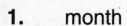

Phonics: Consonant Digraphs
Circle the word that names the picture.
Say the word.

1.   month   meal

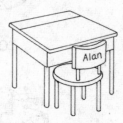

2.   chore   chair

3.   fish   fig

4.   whales   watch

Circle each word with *tch, sh, th* or *ph*.
Write the word on the line.

5.   wash   waste   _____

6.   tree   both   _____

7.   catch   cat   _____

8.   graph   grab   _____

Read the Decodable Reader *At Home in Nome* with a partner.

Beginning/Intermediate Read and point to the words in examples 1–4.
Have partners repeat them to each other. Review word meaning.

Name _____

**Use the word chart to study this week's vocabulary words.
Write a sentence using each word in your writer's notebook.**

Word	Context Sentence	Illustration
patient _____	We are <u>patient</u> as we wait to slide.	
practiced _____	I <u>practiced</u> writing my name in English.	
favorite _____	Mom made my <u>favorite</u> meal.	**What is your favorite meal?**
wrinkled _____	My dog has a <u>wrinkled</u> face.	
settled _____	I am <u>settled</u> in a chair with a good book.	
cuddle _____	I like to <u>cuddle</u> my dog.	

© Macmillan/McGraw-Hill

Beginning/Intermediate Review vocabulary. Use gestures to demonstrate meaning. Pair children to write sentences, or draw pictures, to illustrate the meaning of the newly acquired vocabulary and tell sentences to each other.

Name _____

Grammar: Sentence Combining
Combine the sentences.

1. Lions run. Tigers run.

_____

2. Billy sleeps. Billy wakes up.

_____

3. Julie has a bike. She has a book.

_____

Look at the picture. Write one sentence about the girl and one sentence about the boy. Then combine the sentences.

_____

_____

Beginning/Intermediate Read the directions for each section and model the first example. Have children work with partners to write their sentences. Have them share their sentences with the group.

Read each question and prompt. Discuss the answers with your group. Use *My Name Is Yoon* to find details to support your answers. Then write your answers on the blank lines or on another sheet of paper.

1. What does Yoon mean in Korean?

   _____

2. Tell why Yoon does not want to learn to write her name in English.

   _____

3. Do you think that Yoon will like the new spelling of her name at the end of the story? Explain.

   _____

4. Describe how Yoon's teacher helped her feel better.

   _____

5. Do you think Yoon will make other friends in school?

   _____

6. Write one question about *My Name Is Yoon* to ask your group.

   _____

   _____

Beginning/Intermediate Read the directions. Pair children to answer the questions using basic and content vocabulary. Have them share answers with the group. If needed, they can listen to the selection on **StudentsWork Plus Online**.

Grade 2 Unit I Week 5   25

Name _____

Phonics/Word Study: Long *a*

Circle the word with the long *a* sound.

1.

tooth

train

2.

rain

read

3.

pen

pear

4.

nail

nest

Circle the word with the long *a* sound.

Then write the word on the line. Say the word.

5. corn   tail   there   _____

6. play   pat   sun   _____

Beginning/Intermediate Review how to decode words. Read and point to two words with the long *a* sound (*train, rain*). Point out your mouth position. Have children say the words with a partner. Children can listen to the **Sound Pronunciation CD.**

Name_____

Phonics: Consonant Blends

Circle the word that names the picture.

1. stain   step   strawberry

2. scrap   short   speak

3. play   stay   spray

4. strong   song   speak

Circle each word with *scr*, *spr*, or *str*. Then write the word on the line. Say the word.

5. strike   sock   _____

6. beach   spread   _____

7. spring   sing   _____

8. alone   scrape   _____

Read the Decodable Reader *Watch the Birch Tree* with a partner.

© Macmillan/McGraw-Hill

Beginning/Intermediate Read and point to examples 1–4. Have partners complete all the examples and say words 5–8 to each other.

Name _____

Use the word chart to study this week's vocabulary words.
Write a sentence using each word in your writer's notebook.

Word	Context Sentence	Illustration
exclaimed _____	"She scored another goal!" Dad <u>exclaimed</u>.	
concern _____	My mother's <u>concern</u> was that I broke my leg.	**When might you have concern for someone?**
vendors _____	The food <u>vendors</u> sold hot dogs, ice cream, and popcorn.	HOT DOGS ICE CREAM POPCORN
figure _____	The prize was a <u>figure</u> of a soccer player scoring a goal.	
collection _____	My brother has a <u>collection</u> of stamps from all over the world.	**What kind of a collection would you rather have —stamps or shells?**

Beginning/Intermediate Review vocabulary. Use gestures to demonstrate meaning. Pair children to write sentences, or draw pictures, to illustrate the meaning of the newly acquired vocabulary and tell sentences to each other.

Name_____

Grammar: Nouns

Circle all the nouns in each sentence.

1. Julia eats salad for dinner.

2. The children are playing with the ball.

3. Raj rides his bike everyday.

4. Trees have leaves and roots.

Write a sentence about the picture. Circle each noun in your sentence.

_____

_____

Beginning/Intermediate Read the directions for each section and model the first example. Have children work with partners to circle the nouns and write a sentence. Have them share their sentence with the group.

Read each question and prompt. Discuss the answers with your group. Use _Babu's Song_ to find details to support your answers. Then write your answers on the blank lines or on another sheet of paper.

1. Tell what sport kids play in _Babu's Song_.

_____

2. Explain the problem the main character has.

_____

3. Tell who helped Bernardi in your book.

_____

4. Describe what Bernardi learned to do.

_____

5. Tell who in your book is a hero. Why?

_____

6. Write one question about _Babu's Song_ to ask your group.

_____

_____

Beginning/Intermediate Read the directions. Pair children to answer the questions using basic and content vocabulary. Have them share answers with the group. If needed, they can listen to the selection on **StudentsWork Plus Online**.

Name_____

Phonics/Word Study: Long *e*
Circle the word with the long e sound.
Say the word.

1.   seal

sing

2.   bed

bee

3.   tree

ten

Circle the word with the long e sound.
Write the word on the line.

4. chase   chief   _____

5. eat   full   _____

6. laugh   baby   _____

Read the Decodable Reader *Franny's Rain Forest* with a partner.

© Macmillan/McGraw-Hill

Beginning/Intermediate Review how to decode words. Read and point to two words with the long e sound (*seal, bee*). Point out your mouth position. Have children say the words and listen to the **Sound Pronunciation CD**.

Name _____

Phonics: Prefixes *re-, un-, dis-*
Underline the words that have prefixes. Then write the words.

1. Pam seems unable to start her day.

   _____

2. Her hair is uncombed.

   _____

3. Her mother is displeased.

   _____

4. "Let's restart the day," says her mother.

   _____

5. Pam disappears into her room.

   _____

6. Then she reappears in new clothes.

   _____

7. "Now I will redo everything," says Pam.

   _____

8. Pam will replace a bad day with a good one.

   _____

Read the Decodable Reader *It Won't Be Easy!* with a partner.

Beginning/Intermediate For each sound, say one word for children to repeat. Read the directions and model the first example.

Name _____

Use the word chart to study this week's vocabulary words.
Write a sentence using each word in your writer's notebook.

Word	Context Sentence	Illustration
advice _____	The coach gave me good <u>advice</u>.	**Who else might give you advice?**
commotion _____	Our dog makes a <u>commotion</u> when the phone rings.	
rattled _____	The branches <u>rattled</u> against the window when the wind blew.	
respected _____	Everyone <u>respected</u> the famous scientist.	**Name someone you respect. Why?**
shivering _____	I was <u>shivering</u> in my thin jacket.	
tangle _____	The kittens turned the balls of yarn into a messy <u>tangle</u>.	

Beginning/Intermediate Review vocabulary. Use gestures to demonstrate meaning.
Pair children to write sentences, or draw pictures, to illustrate the meaning of the newly
acquired vocabulary and tell sentences to each other.

Name _____

Grammar: Plural Nouns

Circle the words that name more than one.

1. brushes   boy   baby

2. books   pages   family

3. kittens   puppy   mess

Write a plural noun for each picture.

4.

_____

5.

_____

6.

_____

7.

_____

Beginning/Intermediate Read the directions for each section and model examples 1 and 4. Have children work with partners to complete the examples. Have them say the plural nouns to each other.

Read each question and prompt. Discuss the answers with your group. Use *Doña Flor* to find details to support your answers. Then write your answers on the blank lines or on another sheet of paper.

1. How did Doña Flor help her friends when she was growing up?

   _____

2. What scared her neighbors one spring night?

   _____

3. How did Doña Flor help her scared neighbors?

   _____

4. What advice did the animals give Doña Flor?

   _____

5. What was the cause of all the noise?

   _____

6. How was this story real? How was it not real?

   _____

   _____

Beginning/Intermediate Read the directions. Pair children to answer the questions using basic and content vocabulary. Have them share answers with the group. If needed, they can listen to the selection on **StudentsWork Plus Online.**

Grade 2 Unit 2 Week 2 35

Name _____

Phonics/Word Study: Long *i*
Circle the word with the long *i* sound.

1.

   cry   cup

2.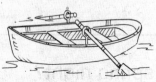

   boat   sky

3.

   pie   dish

4.

   night   nail

Circle the word with the long *i* sound.
Then write the word on the line. Say the word.

5.   tie   the   _____

6.   lamp   light   _____

7.   fight   new   _____

Beginning/Intermediate Review how to decode words. Read and point to two words with the long *i* sound (*cry, sky*). Point out your mouth position. Have children say the words. Children can listen to the **Sound Pronunciation CD**.

Name_____

Phonics: Compound Words

**Add the two words in each row to make a
compound word. Say the word.**

1. snow   +   storm   = _____

2. chalk   +   board   = _____

3. play   +   ground   = _____

4. dog   +   house   = _____

5. grass   +   lands   = _____

Write a word from the box to make a compound word.
Write the new word on the line.

| bed | week | fast |

6. _____ + end   = _____

7. _____ + room   = _____

8. break + _____   = _____

Beginning/Intermediate For each section, read the directions and
model the first example. Have partners say the words to each other.
Have children listen to the **Sound Pronunciation CD.**

Use the word chart to study this week's vocabulary words.
Write a sentence using each word in your writer's notebook.

Word	Context Sentence	Illustration
independence _____	My dad walks to school with me. Teenagers have the <u>independence</u> to walk to school alone.	**How else do teenagers show their independence?**
landmark _____	Visitors take a boat to see this <u>landmark</u>.	
state _____	Texas is the name of the <u>state</u> where we live.	TEXAS **What is the name of another state?**
government _____	The U.S. Capitol is an important <u>government</u> building.	
symbol _____	This <u>symbol</u> stands for "Poison."	

Beginning/Intermediate Review vocabulary. Use gestures to demonstrate meaning. Pair children to write sentences, or draw pictures, to illustrate the meaning of the newly acquired vocabulary and tell sentences to each other.

Name_____

Grammar: Proper Nouns
Circle all the proper nouns.

1. My friend lives in Chicago.

2. Mr. Brown teaches at my school.

3. Doctor Hall helped Julie feel better.

4. Jim works at Riverdale Hospital.

Write your name and the name of your school on the lines.

_____

_____

Beginning/Intermediate Read the directions for each section and model the first example. Have partners complete examples 2–4. Have each child complete the bottom section and read their names to a partner.

Grade 2 Unit 2 Week 3 39

Read each question and prompt. Discuss the answers with your group. Use *A Tall Tale* to find details to support your answers. Then write your answers on the blank lines or on another sheet of paper.

1. Why is the San Jacinto Monument important?

   _____

2. Why was a battle fought at San Jacinto long ago?

   _____

3. How was the San Jacinto Monument built?

   _____

4. What do the doors of the Monument tell us?

   _____

5. Why might you like to visit this Monument?

   _____

6. Tell your group about other monuments you might like to visit.

   _____

   _____

Beginning/Intermediate Read the directions. Pair children to answer the questions using basic and content vocabulary. Have them share answers with the group. If needed, they can listen to the selection on **StudentsWork Plus Online**.

Phonics /Word Study: Long *o*
Circle the word that names the picture.
Then write the word on the line.

1. _____

   bowl   ball

2. _____

   coach   cot

3. _____

   dot   doe

Underline the word with the long o sound. Say the word.

4.	soap	sun	sand
5.	three	toe	that
6.	get	got	goat
7.	take	throw	took

Beginning/Intermediate Review how to decode words. Read and point to the first three words with the long o sound. Point out your mouth position. Have children say the words and listen to the **Sound Pronunciation CD**.

Grade 2 Unit 2 Week 4 41

Name _____

Phonics: Inflectional Endings

**Circle the word that completes each sentence.
Write the word on the line.**

1. Yaks live high in the _____.

   mountains   mountain

2. Many other _____ also live in
   the mountains.

   animal   animals

3. Yaks are great _____.

   beast   beasts

4. They have a lot of fur and long _____.

   horns   horn

Write the new word on the line. Say the word.

5. field + s = _____

6. bus + es = _____

7. puddle + s = _____

8. law + s = _____

Read the Decodable Reader *Three Goats and a Troll* with a partner.

Beginning/Intermediate For each section, read the directions and
model one example. Point out that *buses* ends in *-es*. Have children
listen to the **Sound Pronunciation CD**.

© Macmillan/McGraw-Hill

Name_____

Use the word chart to study this week's vocabulary words. Write a sentence using each word in your writer's notebook.

Word	Context Sentence	Illustration
collectors _____	The collectors looked at the stamps they had gathered.	
store _____	In winter, I store my bike in the shed.	
clever _____	My clever dog brings her leash when she wants to walk.	
reward _____	I reward my dog with a hug when she obeys a command.	**Why might someone be rewarded?**
double _____	John has double the homework of Max.	
amount _____	What amount do I owe you?	

© Macmillan/McGraw-Hill

Beginning/Intermediate Review vocabulary. Use gestures to demonstrate meaning. Pair children to write sentences, or draw pictures, to illustrate the meaning of the newly acquired vocabulary and tell sentences to each other.

Name _____

Grammar: Possessive Nouns
Circle the possessive nouns.

1. bird's   bats   trees

2. teachers   books   girl's

3. friends   mother's   houses

Write the possessive form of the noun in ( ) on the line. Say the sentence.

4. The _____ nest is in the tree.
   (bird)

5. The _____ ears are very big.
   (bat)

6. My _____ birthday is today.
   (friend)

7. The _____ tail is long.
   (horse)

Beginning/Intermediate Read the directions for each section and model examples 1 and 4. Have children work with partners to circle the nouns and complete the sentences. Have them say the sentences to each other.

Name _____

Read each question and prompt. Discuss the answers with your group. Use *One Grain of Rice* to find details to support your answers. Then write your answers on the blank lines or on another sheet of paper.

1. What were the Raja's intentions when he decided to collect so much rice?

    _____

2. Share what you think about Rani's knowledge of math.

    _____

3. What do you think the people in the village will think about Rani?

    _____

4. Explain what you think the Raja will do in the future.

    _____

5. Share something you learned from the story.

    _____

6. Write one question about *One Grain of Rice* to ask your group.

    _____

Beginning/Intermediate Read the directions. Pair children to answer the questions using basic and content vocabulary. Have them share answers with the group. If needed, they can listen to the selection on **StudentsWork Plus Online**.

Grade 2 Unit 2 Week 4   45

Name _____

Phonics/Word Study: Long *u*
Circle the word that names the picture.
Write the word on the line.

1.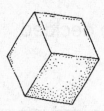

   cube   cup   _____

2.

   fun   mule   _____

3.

   bug   music   _____

4.

   mud   tulip   _____

Circle the word with the long *u* sound. Say the word.

5. comb   cub   cute

6. home   unit   hug

Beginning/Intermediate Review how to decode words. Read and point to two words with the long *u* sound (*cube, mule*). Point out your mouth position. Have children say the words and listen to the **Sound Pronunciation CD**.

Name_____

Phonics: Inflectional Ending *-ing*

Add the ending to the base word. Write the new word on the line.

1. enjoy + ing = _____

2. look + ing = _____

3. delight + ing = _____

4. think + ing = _____

Circle the word that completes the sentence. Write the word on the line. Say the sentence.

5. She is _____ her favorite book.

   read   reading

6. The children are _____ basketball.

   played   playing

7. Kim is _____ to play the piano.

   learned   learning

8. The horse is _____ over the fence.

   jumped   jumping

Read the Decodable Reader *Luke's Tune* with a partner.

Beginning/Intermediate For each section, read the directions and model an example. Have partners say the sentences to each other. Have children listen to the **Sound Pronunciation CD**.

Name _____

Use the word chart to study this week's vocabulary words.
Write a sentence using each word in your writer's notebook.

Word	Context Sentence	Illustration
allowed _____	We are not <u>allowed</u> to wear baseball caps in school.	**Describe things you are not allowed to do in school.**
powerful _____	Many trees fell during the <u>powerful</u> winter storm.	
invented _____	Thomas Edison <u>invented</u> the light bulb.	
instrument _____	The dentist used a special <u>instrument</u> to clean my teeth.	
products _____	We bought paper <u>products</u> for the picnic.	
design _____	The mittens have a snowflake <u>design</u>.	

© Macmillan/McGraw-Hill

Beginning/Intermediate Review vocabulary. Use gestures to demonstrate meaning. Pair children to write sentences, or draw pictures, to illustrate the meaning of the newly acquired vocabulary and tell sentences to each other.

Name_____

Grammar: Plurals and Possessives

Circle the possessive or plural word that completes the sentence. Then write that word on the line.

1. My _____ house is nearby.

    uncles   uncle's

2. The _____ go to the library after school.

    boys   boy's

3. Your _____ are too loud at night.

    dogs   dog's

Write the possessive form of the plural noun in ( ) to complete the sentence.

4. Have you seen the _____ cafeteria?

    (teachers)

5. My _____ car is in the garage.

    (parents)

6. The baseball _____ bats are new.

    (players)

Beginning/Intermediate Read the directions for each section and model examples I and 4. Have children work with partners to circle the nouns and complete the sentences. Have them say sentences 4–6 to each other.

Grade 2 Unit 2 Week 5   49

Name _____

**Read each question and prompt. Discuss the answers
with your group. Use *African-American Inventors* to
find details to support your answers. Then write your
answers on the blank lines or on another sheet of paper.**

1. Compare the inventions of Benjamin Banneker and
   Sarah E. Goode. How are they different?

   _____

2. Compare the inventions of Benjamin Banneker and
   George Washington Carver. How are they alike?

   _____

3. How did the invention of Dr. Patricia Bath help people?
   Explain.

   _____

4. List some of the products that you can make out of sweet
   potatoes and those you can make out of peanuts.

   _____

5. What is your favorite invention in the story?

   _____

6. Write one question about *African-American Inventors* to ask
   your group.

   _____

Beginning/Intermediate Read the directions. Pair children to answer the
questions using basic and content vocabulary. Have them share answers with the
group. If needed, they can listen to the selection on **StudentWorks Plus Online**.

Name _____

Phonics/Word Study: *r*-Controlled Vowels: *er, ir, ur*
Circle the word that names the picture. Say the word.

1. girl   gate   grow

2. fat   fern   feet

3. hat   hand   hurt

4. skate   skin   skirt

Circle the word with *er, ir,* or *ur*.
Write the word on the line.

5. verb   real   _____

6. burn   bite   _____

7. cake   circle   _____

8. herd   hen   _____

Beginning/Intermediate Review how to decode words. In each section, read and point to one word with the new sound. Point out your mouth position. Have children say the words and listen to the **Sound Pronunciation CD**.

Name _____

Phonics: Inflectional Endings *-er, -est*
Circle a word to complete each sentence.

1. That story was the _____ one in the book.

   sadder   saddest

2. This puddle is _____ than that one.

   wider   widest

3. Giraffes are _____ than bears.

   bigger   biggest

4. Abdullah thinks math is the _____ subject.

   harder   hardest

Circle the ending that completes the word in dark print.
Write the ending on the line. Say the sentence.

5. Marie is the **fast** _____ runner in the class.

   er   est

6. Spring is **warm** _____ than winter.

   er   est

7. Bob is the **tall** _____ player on the team.

   er   est

Read the Decodable Reader *Shirl and Her Tern* with a partner.

Beginning/Intermediate Model examples 1 and 5 and say the words for children to repeat. Have partners complete the page and read the sentences to each other.

Name _____

Use the word chart to study this week's vocabulary words. Write a sentence using each word in your writer's notebook.

Word	Context Sentence	Illustration
perform _____	I feel nervous when I perform in front of people.	
effort _____	Learning to play the piano well takes a lot of effort.	 **Describe some things that take a lot of effort to do.**
remember _____	I put my piano music by the door so I would remember it.	
mood _____	The funny song put me in a good mood.	 **Which would put you in a bad mood—watching a funny movie or doing extra homework?**
proud _____	I am proud of the painting I made for Mom.	

© Macmillan/McGraw-Hill

Beginning/Intermediate Review vocabulary. Use gestures to demonstrate meaning. Pair children to write sentences or draw pictures to illustrate the meaning of the newly acquired vocabulary. Have them say sentences to each other.

Name _____

Grammar: Action Verbs

Circle the action verb in each sentence.
Say the sentences.

1. The elf talks to the woodcutter.

2. He wants some food.

3. The woodcutter wastes the wishes.

4. His wife yells at him.

Write two sentences with action verbs to tell what is happening in the picture.

5. _____

6. _____

Beginning/Intermediate Read each set of directions and model the first example. Have partners circle the verbs and write the sentences together. Have children share their sentences with the group.

Read each question and prompt. Discuss the answers with your group. Use *The Alvin Ailey Kids: Dancing As a Team* to find details to support your answers. Then write your answers on the blank lines or on another sheet of paper.

1. Tell what you learned in the selection.

   _____

2. Why is team work important for the dance?

   _____

3. Talk about the many people who help with the performance.

   _____

4. Summarize what the performance was like.

   _____

5. What did you find most interesting about the Ailey School?

   _____

6. Write one question about *The Alvin Ailey Kids: Dancing As a Team* to ask your group.

   _____

   _____

   _____

Beginning/Intermediate Read the directions. Pair children to answer the questions using basic and content vocabulary. Have them share answers with the group. If needed, they can listen to the selection on **StudentsWork Plus Online**.

Grade 2 Unit 3 Week I 55

Name _____

Phonics/Word Study: *r*-Controlled Vowels: *eer, ere, ear*
Circle the word that names each picture.

1.   door   desk   deer

2.   ear   are   car

3.   teeth   tray   tear

Circle the word with the *-er* sound as in *Cheer*.
Write the word on the line. Say the word.

4.   clean   clear   close   _____

5.   new   next   near   _____

6.   her   here   him   _____

7.   sheer   she   sheep   _____

Beginning/Intermediate Read each set of directions. Model examples 1 and 4. Say each word for children to repeat. Have partners complete the examples and say the words. Children can listen to the **Sound Pronunciation CD**.

Name_____

Phonics: Silent Letters

Circle the word that names each picture.
Say the word.

1.

knee   nap

2.

note   knob

3.

gnat   nail

4.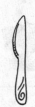

knife   kite

Circle the word with the *m* sound. Write it on the line.

5. test   lamb   curve   _____

6. song   circle   climb   _____

Circle the word with the *r* sound. Write it on the line.

7. write   bite   light   _____

8. apple   wrong   wing   _____

Read the Decodable Reader *Hide and Seek* with a partner.

© Macmillan/McGraw-Hill

Beginning/Intermediate For each section, read the directions and model the first example. Have partners say the words to each other.

Grade 2 Unit 3 Week 2   57

Name_____

Use the word chart to study this week's vocabulary words.
Write a sentence using each word in your writer's notebook.

Word	Context Sentence	Illustration
medium _____	I picked the <u>medium</u> ice-cream cone.	
stubborn _____	The <u>stubborn</u> puppy would not go for a walk.	**Does a stubborn person listen to advice?**
noticed _____	Sue <u>noticed</u> a hole in her favorite sweater.	
cozy _____	The cat looks <u>cozy</u> sleeping in the chair.	**What is a synonym for cozy?**
arrive _____	The guests <u>arrived</u> at 1:00.	
argue _____	Sam and Tim <u>argued</u> about who would play with the ball.	

Beginning/Intermediate Review vocabulary. Use gestures to demonstrate meaning. Pair children to write sentences or draw pictures to illustrate the meaning of the newly acquired vocabulary. Have them say sentences to each other.

Name_____

Grammar: Present-Tense Verbs

Circle the present-tense verb that tells about the picture. Then write the word on the line. Say the sentence.

1. He _____ water on hot days.

   drink   drinks

2. She _____ her book.

   reads   read

3. He _____ his hands before he eats.

   wash   washes

Underline the present-tense verb in each sentence.

4. The girl helps her mother in the kitchen.

5. She plays with her toys every day.

6. He works with an adult in the garden.

7. My mom watches me swim.

© Macmillan/McGraw-Hill

Beginning/Intermediate Read the directions for each section and model examples 1 and 4. Have children work with partners to circle the verbs and complete the sentences. Have them say the sentences to each other.

Grade 2 Unit 3 Week 2   59

Name_____

**Read each question and prompt. Discuss the
answers with your group. Use *Abuelo and the
Three Bears* to find details to support your answers.
Then write your answers on the blank lines or on
another sheet of paper.**

1. Talk about Emilio's problem in the story.

   _____

2. How did Abuelo help Emilio solve his problem?

   _____

3. Summarize the story Abuelo told Emilio.

   _____

4. What did Emilio learn from Abuelo's story?

   _____

5. Share your favorite picture in the story.

   _____

6. Write one question about *Abuelo and the Three Bears* to
   ask your group.

   _____

   _____

Beginning/Intermediate Read the directions. Pair children to answer the questions
using basic and content vocabulary. Have them share answers with the group. If
needed, they can listen to the selection on **StudentsWork Plus Online**.

Name_____

Phonics/Word Study: *r*-Controlled Vowels: *ar*
Circle the word that names the picture.

1. bark   bake   bean

2. sun   shirt   star

3. shake   shark   sat

4. can   crop   card

Circle the word in each pair with the *ar* sound.
Write the word on the line. Say the word.

5. barn   burn   _____

6. cat   cart   _____

7. heat   hard   _____

8. farm   fan   _____

© Macmillan/McGraw-Hill

Beginning/Intermediate Read and point to examples 1-4. Have partners complete the page and say words 5-8 to each other.

Grade 2 Unit 3 Week 3   61

Phonics: Inflectional Ending *-ed*
**Write the ending that shows the past-tense form
of each verb in dark print.**

1. The gecko's skin **help** _____ it hide.

2. I **learn** _____ about animals in
   the rainforest.

3. The python **look** _____ at its prey.

4. The animals **stay** _____ away from the
   poison dart frog.

**Choose a word from the box to complete each sentence.
Write the word on the line. Say the sentence.**

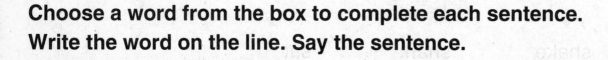

climbed	called	jumped	hunted

5. The jaguar _____ all day.

6. The python _____ up to catch
   the gecko.

7. The gecko _____ off the tree to escape.

8. The top of the rainforest is _____ the canopy.

Read the Decodable Reader *Meg Cage in Space* with a partner.

Beginning/Intermediate Model examples 1 and 5 and say the words
for children to repeat. Have partners complete the page and read the
sentences to each other.

Name_____

Use the word chart to study this week's vocabulary words. Write a sentence using each word in your writer's notebook.

Word	Context Sentence	Illustration
impossible _____	It was <u>impossible</u> to lift the heavy box.	
treasures _____	I put my new necklace in a box with my other <u>treasures</u>.	
talent _____	I think juggling takes a lot of <u>talent</u>.	
pleasant _____	We spent a <u>pleasant</u> day at the beach.	**What would you describe as pleasant?**

Beginning/Intermediate Review vocabulary. Use gestures to demonstrate meaning. Pair children to write sentences or draw pictures to illustrate the meaning of the newly acquired vocabulary. Have them say sentences to each other.

Grade 2 Unit 3 Week 3 (63)

Name _____

Grammar: Past-tense Verbs

Read the sentences below. Circle the past-tense verb in each sentence.

1. I visited the zoo last week.

2. The elephant played in the water.

3. The tigers jumped in the grass.

4. Long ago, people hunted giant tortoises.

Write the past-tense form of the word in dark print.
Say the correct sentence.

5. We **learn** about animals that live a long time. _____

6. The elephant **lift** the man high in the air. _____

7. I **wait** in line to see the monkeys. _____

64 Grade 2 Unit 3 Week 3

Beginning/Intermediate Read the directions for each section and model the first example. Have partners complete examples 2-4. Have each child complete the bottom section and read their sentences to a partner.

Name_____

**Read each question and prompt. Discuss the
answers with your group. Use *Music of the Stone
Age* to find details to support your answers. Then
write your answers on the blank lines or on another
sheet of paper.**

1. Why did the author write *Music of the Stone Age*?

    _____

2. Tell about sound. How is sound made?

    _____

3. How do we know that people long ago played music?

    _____

4. Explain how the flutes found in China were made.

    _____

5. What do you think music sounded like thousands of years
    ago? Share your ideas.

    _____

6. Write one question about *Music of the Stone Age* to ask
    your group.

    _____

    _____

Beginning/Intermediate Read the directions. Pair children to answer the questions
using basic and content vocabulary. Have them share answers with the group. If
needed, they can listen to the selection on **StudentsWork Plus Online**.   Grade 2 Unit 3 Week 3   65

Phonics/Word Study: *r*-Controlled Vowels: *or, ore, oar*
Circle the word that names each picture.

1. cot   car   corn

2. fun   fork   fair

3. home   her   horn

4. shoe   stop   store

Circle the word with the *-or* sound. Write the word on the line. Say the word.

5. ore   only   far   _____

6. for   fun   fit   _____

7. wore   won   why   _____

8. bear   boar   buy   _____

Beginning/Intermediate For each section, read the directions and model the first example. Have partners say the words to each other. Children can listen to the **Sound Pronunciation CD**.

Name_____

Phonics: Suffixes *-er, -est*
Circle the word that completes each sentence.
Write the word on the line.

1. Plastic can be cut into _____ pieces.

   smaller   smallest

2. Some trash is _____ to recycle than other trash.

   hardest   harder

3. Plastic containers take the _____ to break down.

   longer   longest

Circle the ending that completes the word in dark print.
Write the ending on the line. Say the sentence.

4. The landfill was **long** _____ than the playground.

   er   est

5. This garbage can is **light** _____ than that one.

   er   est

   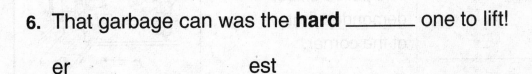

6. That garbage can was the **hard** _____ one to lift!

   er   est

Read the Decodable Reader *More Fun Than a Hat!* with a partner.

© Macmillan/McGraw-Hill

Beginning/Intermediate Read the directions and review how to decode. Read the words and ask children to repeat. Use gestures to demonstrate meaning. Ask children to practice saying these words to a partner.

Grade 2 Unit 3 Week 4 67

Use the word chart to study this week's vocabulary words. Write a sentence using each word in your writer's notebook.

Word	Context Sentence	Illustration
impatient _____	Dad gets <u>impatient</u> when the newspaper is late.	**List what you might do when you feel impatient.**
furious _____	Bill was <u>furious</u> about the mess the dog made.	
neutral _____	Tom doesn't care who wins because he's <u>neutral</u>.	
emergency _____	The fire truck rushed to an <u>emergency</u>.	
demand _____	The police officer <u>demanded</u> that we stop at the corner.	
sincerely _____	I <u>sincerely</u> liked the birthday present.	

© Macmillan/McGraw-Hill

Beginning/Intermediate Review vocabulary. Use gestures to demonstrate meaning. Pair children to write sentences or draw pictures to illustrate the meaning of the newly acquired vocabulary. Have them say sentences to each other.

Name_____

Grammar: The Verb *Have*
Circle the word that completes each sentence. Write the word on the line. Say the sentence.

1. Yesterday Sarah _____ a meeting with her coach.

   has   have   had

2. Sarah and her friends _____ a skating contest every week.

   has   have   had

3. Now she _____ an Olympic gold medal.

   has   have   had

Write *present* or *past* to tell if each word in dark print is in the present tense or in the past tense.

4. Sarah **has** breakfast before she practices. _____

5. Last year, Sarah **had** a lot of fun skating. _____

6. The others skaters **had** fun too. _____

7. The skaters **have** many competitions. _____

Beginning/Intermediate Read the directions for each section and model the first example. Have children work with partners to complete the page. Have them share their sentences with the group.

Grade 2 Unit 3 Week 4   69

**Read each question and prompt. Discuss the
answers with your group. Use *Click, Clack, Moo:
Cows That Type* to find details to support your
answers. Then write your answers on the blank
lines or on another sheet of paper.**

1. Tell about the characters in your book, both the animals and
   the humans.

   _____

2. What causes the cows to go on strike?

   _____

3. How did the cows' behavior affect the ducks?

   _____

4. Tell how the animal characters behave like humans.

   _____

5. Did you find the book to be silly? Did it make you laugh?
   Share your ideas with your classmates.

   _____

6. Write one question about *Click, Clack, Moo: Cows That
   Type* to ask your group.

   _____

   _____

© Macmillan/McGraw-Hill

Beginning/Intermediate Read the directions. Pair children to answer the questions
using basic and content vocabulary. Have them share answers with the group. If
needed, they can listen to the selection on **StudentsWork Plus Online**.

Name_____

Phonics/Word Study: *r*-Controlled Vowels
are, air, ear, ere
Circle the word that names the picture.
Say the word.

1.   beet   bear   bead

2.   can   ear   car

3.   cheese   cheer   chair

4.   scare   scat   steer

Beginning/Intermediate Review how to decode. Point to and name the pictures.
Point out your mouth position. Have children repeat and practice saying the words
with a partner. Have them listen to the **Sound Pronunciation CD**.

Grade 2 Unit 3 Week 5   71

© Macmillan/McGraw-Hill

Name _____

Phonics: Prefixes *re-, un-, dis-*

Add the prefix *re-* to the word in parentheses ( ).
Write the word in the sentence. Say the sentence.

1. I have to (write) _____ my story.

2. I will (think) _____ some of my ideas.

Add the prefix *un-* to the word in parentheses ( ).
Write the word in the sentence. Say the sentence.

3. I am (sure) _____ how to begin.

4. My characters will not be (happy) _____ at the end.

Add the prefix *dis-* to the word in parentheses ( ).
Write the word in the sentence. Say the sentence.

5. My friend likes sad stories, but I (agree) _____.

6. I (like) _____ sad endings.

Read the Decodable Reader *The Caring King's Fair Wish* with a partner.

© Macmillan/McGraw-Hill

Beginning/Intermediate For each section, read the directions and model an example. Have partners say the sentences to each other.

Use the word chart to study this week's vocabulary words. Write a sentence using each word in your writer's notebook.

Word	Context Sentence	Illustration
creating _____	Dad is <u>creating</u> pictures for his story.	
familiar _____	The story was <u>familiar</u>. I'd heard it many times.	
occasions _____	Birthday parties are my favorite family <u>occasions</u>.	
memories _____	Looking at my photo album brings back good <u>memories</u>.	**Describe two of your favorite memories.**
imagination _____	I use my <u>imagination</u> to write stories.	**When might you use your imagination?**
glamorous _____	I dressed up like a <u>glamorous</u> movie star.	

Beginning/Intermediate Review vocabulary. Use gestures to demonstrate meaning. Pair children to write sentences or draw pictures to illustrate the meaning of the newly acquired vocabulary. Have them say sentences to each other.

Grammar: Sentence Combining

Combine the two sentences to make one
sentence. Use *but* or *and* in the new
sentence. Say the sentence.

1. Desi said he didn't know what was happening. He knew.

_____

_____

2. The hens were bored. They did not lay eggs.

_____

3. Mr. Gomez went outside. He saw Ferdie the fox.

_____

4. The hens wanted to have fun. Mr. Gomez was furious.

_____

5. Mr. Gomez said the hens could have fun. They went back to
   the farm.

_____

_____

6. They were never bored. There were always eggs.

_____

_____

Beginning/Intermediate Read the directions and model the first
example. Have children work with partners to write their sentences.
Have them share their sentences with the group.

Read each question and prompt. Discuss the answers with your group. Use *Stirring Up Memories* **to find details to support your answers. Then write your answers on the blank lines or on another sheet of paper.**

1. Discuss the title of the story with your classmates. What does it mean?

   _____

2. Do you think Pam had a happy childhood? Give examples to support your answer.

   _____

3. Why do you think readers always want to know where Pam gets her ideas?

   _____

4. Tell what you learned about how authors get ideas.

   _____

5. What would you like to write about? Share your ideas.

   _____

6. Write one question about *Stirring Up Memories* to ask your group.

   _____

   _____

Beginning/Intermediate Read the directions. Pair children to answer the questions using basic and content vocabulary. Have them share answers with the group. If needed, they can listen to the selection on **StudentsWork Plus Online**.

Grade 2 Unit 3 Week 5 75

Name _____

Phonics/Word Study: Diphthong *ou, ow*
Circle the word that names each picture.

1.

   crown   cone

2.

   bus   blouse

3.

   couch   coach

4.

   foot   frown

Circle the word with the /ou/ sound. Write the word on the line. Say the word.

5.   towel   tool   tune   _____

6.   hole   how   hand   _____

7.   moss   mouse   most   _____

8.   boys   ball   bounce   _____

Beginning/Intermediate Review how to decode words. Read and point to two words with the /ou/ sound. Point out your mouth position. Have children say the words and listen to the **Sound Pronunciation CD**.

Name_____

Phonics: Inflectional Endings -s, -es
Change each word to mean more than one.
Write the new word on the line. Say the new word.

1. zoo   _____

2. berry   _____

3. patch   _____

4. kite   _____

5. baby   _____

6. fox   _____

7. bus   _____

8. friend   _____

Read the Decodable Reader *The Missing String Beans* with a partner.

Beginning/Intermediate Read the directions and model in examples
1–3. Have children work with partners to complete the page.

Grade 2 Unit 4 Week 1 77

© Macmillan/McGraw-Hill

Name _____

Use the word chart to study this week's vocabulary words.
Write a sentence using each word in your writer's notebook.

Word	Context Sentence	Illustration
gasped _____	We gasped when we saw the size of the huge spider.	**What has made you gasp?**
attached _____	We wondered if a fish would be attached to the hook.	
frantically _____	Jack and I looked frantically for his missing cat.	
swung _____	We watched as the monkey swung from branch to branch.	
delicious _____	Together, we made a delicious meal.	**What would you describe as delicious?**

© Macmillan/McGraw-Hill

Beginning/Intermediate Review vocabulary. Use gestures to demonstrate meaning. Pair children to write sentences or draw pictures to illustrate the meaning of the newly acquired vocabulary. Have them say sentences to each other.

Name_____

Grammar: Linking Verbs

Underline the linking verb in each sentence.

1. An ox is very big.

2. Roosters are loud animals.

3. The ox was in the field.

4. The farm animals were warm in winter.

Write two sentences. Use a linking verb in each sentence. Then circle each linking verb.

5. _____

_____

6. _____

_____

Beginning/Intermediate Read the directions for each section and model the first example. Have partners complete examples 2–4. Have each child complete the bottom section and read their sentences to a partner.

Read each question and prompt. Discuss the answers with your group. Use *Head, Body, Legs* to find details to support your answers. Then write your answers on the blank lines or on another sheet of paper.

1. Talk about the characters in *Head, Body, Legs*.

   _____

2. Tell about the problem Head had.

   _____

3. What caused Arms to join Head?

   _____

4. What happened when all the parts worked together?

   _____

5. Share what you think is the most interesting part of the story.

   _____

6. Write one question about *Head, Body, Legs* to ask your group.

   _____

   _____

   _____

Beginning/Intermediate Read the directions. Pair children to answer the questions using basic and content vocabulary. Have them share answers with the group. If needed, they can listen to the selection on **StudentsWork Plus Online.**

Name_____

Phonics/Word Study: Diphthong /oi/: *oi, oy*
Circle the word that names each picture.

1.    coin   cone

2.   toys   two

3.    bowl   boil

Circle the word with the /oi/ sound.
Write the word on the line. Say the word.

4. old   oil   on   _____

5. voice   vote   very   _____

6. fold   fool   foil   _____

7. boy   bow   bay   _____

8. choice choose chop   _____

Beginning/Intermediate Review how to decode words. Read and point to two words with the */oi/* sound. Point out your mouth position. Have children say the words and listen to the **Sound Pronunciation CD.**

Grade 2 Unit 4 Week 2   81

Phonics: Prefixes *re-, un-, dis-*
Circle the prefix in each underlined word. Then circle the meaning of the word.

1. We had an <u>unhappy</u> time last night.

   not happy   happy again

2. We <u>revisited</u> a pizza restaurant.

   did not visit   visited again

3. We <u>disagreed</u> about what pizza to get.

   did not agree   agreed again

4. Then Mom said she <u>disliked</u> pizza anyway.

   liked again   did not like

5. She was <u>unsure</u> what to order.

   not sure   sure again

6. Her soup came cold. The chef had to <u>reheat</u> it.

   not heat   heat again

7. The waiter dropped our pizza. The chef <u>remade</u> it.

   made again   did not make

Read the Decodable Reader *Let's Join Joy's Show!* with a partner.

Beginning/Intermediate Say words for each prefix and have children repeat. Have partners complete and read sentences to each other.

Name_____

Use the word chart to study this week's vocabulary words.
Write a sentence using each word in your writer's notebook.

Word	Context Sentence	Illustration
attention _____	Sam was not paying <u>attention</u> to where he was going.	
buddy _____	I walk to school with my <u>buddy</u> Jack.	
accident _____	Tie your shoelaces so you don't trip and have an <u>accident</u>.	
tip _____	Washing your hands before you eat is a good <u>tip</u> for staying healthy.	
enormous _____	I felt small next to the <u>enormous</u> tree.	**What is another word for enormous?**
obeys _____	My dog <u>obeys</u> me when I tell him to sit.	

Beginning/Intermediate Review vocabulary. Use gestures to demonstrate meaning. Pair children to write sentences or draw pictures to illustrate the meaning of the newly acquired vocabulary. Have them say sentences to each other.

Name _____

Grammar: Helping Verbs

Circle the helping verb in each sentence.
Say the sentence.

1. The dolphin is jumping.

2. I have seen dolphins in the ocean.

3. The rangers are helping the dolphin.

4. She has saved many animals.

Circle the helping verb that completes each sentence.

5. Angie _____ helping her grandmother.

   is   are

6. They _____ visited the aquarium before.

   has   have

7. She _____ eaten breakfast.

   has   have

8. The people _____ watching the bears.

   is   are

Beginning/Intermediate Read the directions for each section and model examples 1 and 5. Have children work with partners to circle the verbs and complete the sentences. Have them say the sentences to each other.

Read each question and prompt. Discuss the answers with your group. Use *Officer Buckle and Gloria* to find details to support your answers. Then write your answers on the blank lines or on another sheet of paper.

1. Did the students at Napville School need to learn about safety tips? Use the illustrations to support your answer.

_____

2. Describe how Gloria made the students listen to Officer Buckle.

_____

3. List some of the safety tips mentioned in *Officer Buckle and Gloria.*

_____

4. Look at the illustration of Gloria sitting onstage by herself. How do you think she feels?

_____

5. What was Mrs. Toppel doing when the biggest accident in Napville School happened?

_____

6. Write one question about *Officer Buckle and Gloria* to ask your group.

_____

Beginning/Intermediate Read the directions. Pair children to answer the questions using basic and content vocabulary. Have them share answers with the group. If needed, they can listen to the selection on **StudentsWork Plus Online**.

Grade 2 Unit 4 Week 2 85

© Macmillan/McGraw-Hill

Name _____

Phonics/Word Study: Vowel Digraph /ü/

Circle the word that names the picture.

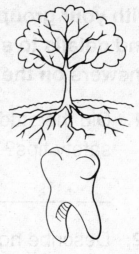

1. roots   rode   run

2. toe   tooth   ten

3. fan   friend   fruit

4. blew   box   bend

Circle the word with the /ü/ sound as in *boot*.
Write the word on the line. Say the word.

5. soon   son   _____

6. gone   grew   _____

7. juice   jump   _____

8. salt   suit   _____

Beginning/Intermediate Review how to decode. Point to and name the pictures. Point out your mouth position. Have children repeat and practice saying the words with a partner. Have them listen to the **Sound Pronunciation CD**.

Name_____

Phonics: Suffixes *-ful, -less*
Write the new word on the line. Say the word.

1. color + ful   = _____

2. power + less   = _____

3. wonder + ful   = _____

Circle the meaning of the word in dark print to complete each sentence.

4. The word **fearless** means _____.

   full of fear   without fear

5. The word **painful** means _____.

   full of power   full of pain

6. The word **joyful** means _____.

   without joy   full of joy

Circle the word in ( ) that best completes each sentence.

7. Superheroes are very (powerful, fearful) characters.

8. I like to wear (painful, colorful) clothes.

Read the Decodable Reader *Soon the North Wind Blew* **with a partner.**

Beginning/Intermediate Model examples 1, 4, and 7 and say the words for children to repeat. Have partners complete the page and read the sentences to each other.

Name_____

Use the word chart to study this week's vocabulary words. Write a sentence using each word in your writer's notebook.

Word	Context Sentence	Illustration
serious _____	The police officer has a <u>serious</u> look on her face.	**When should you act in a serious way?**
personal _____	The doctor was <u>personal</u>. She really cared.	
aid _____	Nurses give <u>aid</u> to sick people.	
informs _____	The officer <u>informs</u> us about bicycle safety.	**What else might a police officer inform you about?**
heal _____	It took a long time for the cut on my arm to <u>heal</u>.	

Beginning/Intermediate Review vocabulary. Use gestures to demonstrate meaning. Pair children to write sentences or draw pictures to illustrate the meaning of the newly acquired vocabulary. Have them say sentences to each other.

Name_____

Grammar: Irregular Verbs

Circle the past-tense verb that completes each sentence. Write the word on the line.

1. Yesterday we _____ to a recycling center.

   went   go

2. We _____ away a lot of trash.

   throw   threw

3. A truck _____ the trash to a landfill.

   took   takes

4. The trash _____ down in the landfill.

   break   broke

Write a word from the box to complete each sentence. Say the sentence.

grew	made	had	put

5. I _____ fun planting a garden.

6. We _____ seeds in the soil.

7. The rain _____ the plants grow.

8. All of the plants in our garden _____ well.

Beginning/Intermediate Read the directions for each section and model the first example. Have children work with partners to complete the page. Have them share their sentences with the group.

Name _____

Read each question and prompt. Discuss the answers with your group. Use *A Trip to the Emergency Room* to find details to support your answers. Then write your answers on the blank lines or on another sheet of paper.

1. Talk about why the emergency room is important.

   _____

2. Tell what happens when a person goes to the emergency room. List the steps in order.

   _____

3. Who sees you first when you go to the emergency room, a doctor or a nurse?

   _____

4. Describe the jobs of the people who work at the emergency room.

   _____

5. Would you like to work at an emergency room? Why or why not?

   _____

6. Write one question about *A Trip to the Emergency Room* to ask your group.

   _____

Beginning/Intermediate Read the directions. Pair children to answer the questions using basic and content vocabulary. Have them share answers with the group. If needed, they can listen to the selection on **StudentsWork Plus Online**.

Name_____

Phonics/Word Study: Vowel Digraph /ù/ (*oo, ou*)
Circle the word that names the picture.

1. cook   caught   coin

2. bone   boy   book

3. home   hook   hole

4. hood   hope   horn

Underline the word in each sentence that has the /ù/ sound as in *good*. Say the sentence.

5. You could help Earth by saving water.

6. People chop down trees to get wood.

7. We should use less trash.

8. Would you help recycle?

Beginning/Intermediate Review how to decode. Point to and name the pictures. Point out your mouth position. Have children repeat and practice saying the words with a partner. Have them listen to the **Sound Pronunciation CD**.

Name _____

Phonics: Inflectional Ending *-ing*

Add *-ing* to the word in parentheses ( ) to make a new word. Write the new word on the line. Say the sentence.

1. The children were _____ in a boat. (ride)

2. They were _____ a trip. (take)

3. They were _____ out at the ocean. (gaze)

4. They were _____ to see whales. (hope)

5. Suddenly whales were _____ near the boat. (move)

6. The whales were _____ closer. (come)

7. They were _____ big waves. (make)

8. The whales were _____ quite a show. (give)

Read the Decodable Reader *Flip and Spots* with a partner.

© Macmillan/McGraw-Hill

Beginning/Intermediate Read the directions and model an example.
Have partners say the sentences to each other.

Name _____

**Use the word chart to study this week's vocabulary words.
Write a sentence using each word in your writer's notebook.**

Word	Context Sentence	Illustration
young _____	The young bird fell from the nest and needed help.	
examines _____	The doctor takes her time when she examines her patient.	
mammal _____	Today in school we learned about mammals.	
normal _____	It is not normal to see a whale on a beach.	
hunger _____	An animal will feel hunger if it cannot find food.	
rescued _____	The firefighter rescued the cat from the tree.	 **Why might someone need to be rescued at the beach?**

Beginning/Intermediate Review vocabulary. Use gestures to demonstrate meaning. Pair children to write sentences or draw pictures to illustrate the meaning of the newly acquired vocabulary. Have them say sentences to each other.

Grammar: Irregular Verbs
Circle the verb that shows the past tense.
Write the word on the line.

1. Alex _____ his sled in the yard.

   leave   leaf   left

2. Alex _____ a TV show about lions.

   saw   seed   see

3. Alex and his mom _____ a new sled.

   make   mad   made

4. Alex _____ the sled race!

   wind   win   won

Write a word from the box to complete each sentence.
Say each sentence.

drew	told	rode

5. Yesterday I _____ my bike.

6. We _____ pictures when it rained.

7. My brother _____ me a story.

Beginning/Intermediate Read the directions for each section and model the first example. Have children work with partners to complete the sentences. Have them share their sentences with the group.

Read each question and prompt. Discuss the answers with your group. Use *A Harbor Seal Pup Grows Up* to find details to support your answers. Then write your answers on the blank lines or on another sheet of paper.

1. Why was Sidney brought to the sea mammal center?

_____

2. Describe what Peter and Nicole did to nurse Sidney back to health. List the steps in order.

_____

3. What does Sidney get first, a healthy drink or a fish?

_____

4. Tell how Sidney is returned to the ocean.

_____

5. Share your favorite picture in the story.

_____

6. Write one question about *A Harbor Seal Pup Grows Up* to ask your group.

_____

_____

_____

Beginning/Intermediate Read the directions. Pair children to answer the questions using basic and content vocabulary. Have them share answers with the group. If needed, they can listen to the selection on **StudentsWork Plus Online**.

Grade 2 Unit 4 Week 4   95

Name _____

Phonics/Word Study: Variant Vowel /ô/ (*au, aw, a*)
Circle the word that names the picture. Say the word.

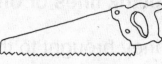

1. set   saw

2. taught   tent

3. land   law

Circle the word that completes each sentence.
Write the word on the line.

4. The dog hurt its _____.

    paw   pet

5. Pedro likes to _____ pictures of animals.

    draw   say

6. Who is the _____ of that book?

    actor   author

7. My sister uses a _____ when she drinks juice.

    store   straw

Beginning/Intermediate Review how to decode. Point to and name the pictures.
Point out your mouth position. Have children repeat and practice saying the words
with a partner. Have them listen to the **Sound Pronunciation CD**.

© Macmillan/McGraw-Hill

Phonics: Inflectional Ending -ed

Add -ed to the word in parentheses ( ) to make a new word. Write the new word on the line. Say the sentence.

1. Jay _____ on a team with Mario. (play)

2. Yesterday I _____ they would win. (hope)

3. They _____ to win their last game. (try)

4. Jay _____ the ball. (pitch)

5. The coach _____ to the boys. (call)

6. "You _____ me good playing today," he said. (show)

Read the Decodable Reader *Paul Saw Arctic Foxes* with a partner.

Beginning/Intermediate Read the directions and model an example.
Have partners complete and then say the sentences to each other.

Grade 2 Unit 4 Week 5 97

Use the word chart to study this week's vocabulary words. Write a sentence using each word in your writer's notebook.

Word	Context Sentence	Illustration
menu　_____	Yum! The picnic <u>menu</u> listed my favorite foods.	**What things might you find on a picnic menu?**
fetch　_____	We went to <u>fetch</u> the food from the house.	**Does fetch mean to catch something or to run and bring it back?**
simmered　_____	The soup <u>simmered</u> for an hour before it was done.	
assembled　_____	We <u>assembled</u> all the food for the picnic.	
devoured　_____	Greg <u>devoured</u> his lunch before anyone else.	

© Macmillan/McGraw-Hill

Beginning/Intermediate Review vocabulary. Use gestures to demonstrate meaning. Pair children to write sentences or draw pictures to illustrate the meaning of the newly acquired vocabulary. Have them say sentences to each other.

Name_____

Grammar: Contractions

Circle the contraction that completes each sentence.
Write the word on the line.

1. The Amazon _____ a desert.

   isnt'   isn't

2. The giant anteater _____ have teeth.

   doesn't   does't

3. _____ fun to watch.

   They're   Theyr'e

4. Tapirs _____ have short noses.

   dont'   don't

Write a contraction for each of the words in dark print.

5. Alan **is not** in class today. _____

6. **They are** hungry. _____

7. My friend **does not** live far away. _____

8. Those children **do not** want to play. _____

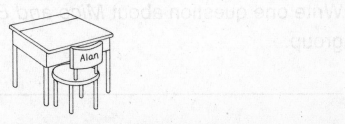

© Macmillan/McGraw-Hill

Read each question and prompt. Discuss the answers with your group. Use _Mice and Beans_ to find details to support your answers. Then write your answers on the blank lines or on another sheet of paper.

1. The main character is getting ready for a party. What kind of a party is it?

   _____

2. Rosa María goes shopping to get ingredients to make dinner for the party. Tell what she had to get.

   _____

3. Talk about the details that make _Mice and Beans_ a fantasy.

   _____

4. Describe something in _Mice and Beans_ that could be based on reality.

   _____

5. What did you learn from _Mice and Beans_? Share with your classmates.

   _____

6. Write one question about _Mice and Beans_ to ask your group.

   _____

Beginning/Intermediate Read the directions. Pair children to answer the questions using basic and content vocabulary. Have them share answers with the group. If needed, they can listen to the selection on **StudentsWork Plus Online**.

Name_____

Phonics/Word Study: Words with Closed Syllables
Put the two syllables together. Write the word. Then draw a picture to show the meaning of the word.

1. kit + ten = _____

2. but + ton = _____

3. pump + kin = _____

4. cac + tus = _____

5. sand + wich = _____

6. in + sect = _____

Beginning/Intermediate Review how to decode. Point to and read the syllables. Point out your mouth position. Have children repeat and practice saying the words with a partner. Have them listen to the **Sound Pronunciation CD**.

Phonics: Words with Closed Syllables

Put the two syllables together. Write the word on the line. Then match the word to the picture it names.

1. dol + lar = _____

2. rab + bit = _____

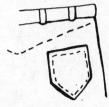

3. muf + fin = _____

4. jack + et = _____

5. pock + et = _____

6. mag + net = _____

Read the Decodable Reader *Judge Marge* with a partner.

Beginning/Intermediate Read the directions and model example 1. Have children complete the page with a partner and say the words to each other.

Name _____

**Use the word chart to study this week's vocabulary words.
Write a sentence using each word in your writer's notebook.**

Word	Context Sentence	Illustration
burst _____	The seed pod <u>burst</u> open, and the seeds flew out.	
drifts _____	A leaf <u>drifts</u> down from the tree.	
desert _____	The <u>desert</u> is hot and dry.	
drowns _____	Do not <u>drown</u> the plant with water.	
gently _____	I <u>gently</u> picked some flowers in the garden.	**When else would you need to do something gently?**
neighbor _____	Our <u>neighbor</u> next door has many plants.	**What is the name of your neighbor?**

Beginning/Intermediate Review vocabulary. Use gestures to demonstrate meaning.
Pair children to write sentences, or draw pictures, to illustrate the meaning of the newly
acquired vocabulary and tell sentences to each other.

Name _____

Grammar: Pronouns

Circle the pronoun in ( ) that takes the place
of the words in dark print. Write the new
sentence on the line.

1. **The rangers** take care of animals.   (It, They)

_____

2. **The desert** is hot and dry.   (It, They)

_____

3. **Tarantulas** live in the Sonoran Desert.   (They, It)

_____

4. **The ocelot** hunts at night.   (They, It)

_____

Write the pronoun *it* or *they* for each word in ( ).

5. (rattlesnakes) _____

6. (cougar)   _____

7. (owls)   _____

Beginning/Intermediate Read the directions. Review pronouns.
Name them and have children repeat. Have children work with a partner
to circle the pronouns, then read the sentences to each other.

Name_____

Read each question and prompt. Discuss the answers with your group. Use *The Tiny Seed* to find details to support your answers. Then write your answers on the blank lines or on another sheet of paper.

1. Name the places that the seeds in *The Tiny Seed* go to.

   _____

2. Explain why the tiny seed cannot grow in the icy mountain.

   _____

3. Talk about something in *The Tiny Seed* that helps you conclude the story is not real.

   _____

4. Discuss the things that can stop the seed from growing.

   _____

5. What will happen to the seeds of the giant flower?

   _____

6. Write one question about *The Tiny Seed* to ask your group.

   _____

   _____

   _____

   _____

Name _____

Phonics/Word Study: Words with Closed Syllables

Draw a line to break each word into syllables. Say the word. Then match the word to the picture it names.

1. cottage

2. ribbon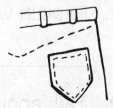

3. hammer

4. wallet

5. pocket

6. napkin

7. princess

Beginning/Intermediate Model example 1 and say the words for children to repeat. Have partners complete the page. Have children listen to the **Sound Pronunciation CD.**

Name_____

Phonics: Words with Closed Syllables

Break each word into syllables. Write the syllables on the lines.

Example: picnic _____pic_____ _____nic_____

1. tennis _____ _____

2. channel _____ _____

3. winter _____ _____

4. welcome _____ _____

5. basket _____ _____

6. kingdom _____ _____

7. hiccup _____ _____

Read the Decodable Reader *Calvin's Pumpin* with a partner.

Beginning/Intermediate Read the directions and model the example. Have children complete the page with a partner and say the words to each other.

Grade 2 Unit 5 Week 2 (107)

Use the word chart to study this week's vocabulary words.
Write a sentence using each word in your writer's notebook.

Word	Context Sentence	Illustration
scent _____	Roses have a sweet <u>scent</u>.	Is a scent something you see or something you smell?
trade _____	She <u>traded</u> a large plant for some apples.	
muscles _____	He has strong <u>muscles</u>.	
prickly _____	This plant has a <u>prickly</u> stem.	
blooming _____	One flower is <u>blooming</u>.	
aroma _____	I love the <u>aroma</u> of our vegetable soup.	What aroma do you like?

Beginning/Intermediate Review vocabulary. Ask children to identify Spanish cognates. Pair children to write sentences, or draw pictures, to illustrate the meaning of the newly acquired vocabulary and tell sentences to each other.

Name_____

Grammar: *I* and *me, we* and *us*
Circle the pronoun that completes each sentence.
Write the pronoun on the line.

1. She gave the book to _____.

   I   me

2. _____ rode our bikes after school.

   Us   We

3. _____ like drawing with colors.

   me   I

4. My brother likes to play with _____.

   we   us

Write a word from the box to complete each sentence.
Say the sentence.

I	We	me

5. _____ went to the library together.

6. _____ don't cross the street alone.

7. My sister goes home with _____.

Beginning/Intermediate Read the directions. Review pronouns. Have children complete the page and share their answers with the class.

Grade 2 Unit 5 Week 2 109

Read each question and prompt. Discuss the answers with your group. Use *The Ugly Vegetables* to find details to support your answers. Then write your answers on the blank lines or on another sheet of paper.

1. Summarize the story *The Ugly Vegetables*.

   _____

2. What did the mother and the girl do first, water the seeds or stick the names of the vegetables?

   _____

3. Describe the steps to grow the vegetable garden in order.

   _____

4. The mother tells the girl that the vegetables are better. Do you agree? Why or why not?

   _____

5. Tell your classmates what your favorite vegetables are.

   _____

6. Write one question about *The Ugly Vegetables* to ask your group.

   _____

   _____

Beginning/Intermediate Read the directions. Pair children to answer the questions using basic and content vocabulary. Have them share answers with the group. If needed, they can listen to the selection on **StudentsWork Plus Online**.

Name_____

Phonics/Word Study: Words with Open Syllables

Draw a line to break each word into syllables.
Then match the word to the picture it names.

1. yoyo

2. paper

3. pony

4. spider

5. pilot

6. acorn

7. zebra

Beginning/Intermediate Review how to decode words. Read the directions and break the first word into syllables. Point out your mouth position. Have children say the words and listen to the **Sound Pronunciation CD**.

Grade 2 Unit 5 Week 3

111

Name _____

Phonics: Words with Open Syllables

Divide each word into syllables. Write the word parts on the lines.

Example: lazy   ____la____   ____zy____

1. baby   _____   _____

2. tiger   _____   _____

3. music   _____   _____

4. open   _____   _____

5. pupil   _____   _____

6. final   _____   _____

7. evil   _____   _____

8. bagel   _____   _____

9. ruby   _____   _____

Read the Decodable Reader *Decode It* with a partner.

© Macmillan/McGraw-Hill

Beginning/Intermediate Read the directions and model the example. Have children complete the page with a partner and say the words to each other.

Name_____

Use the word chart to study this week's vocabulary words. Write a sentence using each word in your writer's notebook.

Word	Context Sentence	Illustration
ancient _____	Dinosaurs lived in an <u>ancient</u> time.	
hopeful _____	Carla is <u>hopeful</u> that she will make a basket.	**What are you hopeful of doing some day?**
unable _____	We were <u>unable</u> to visit the museum.	
confirm _____	Use a dictionary to <u>confirm</u> how a word is spelled.	
valid _____	This answer is not <u>valid</u>.	3+3=6 1+1=2 2+2=5 ✗
site _____	We found a lot of pottery at this <u>site</u>.	

© Macmillan/McGraw-Hill

Beginning/Intermediate Review vocabulary. Ask children to identify Spanish cognates. Pair children to write sentences, or draw pictures, to illustrate the meaning of the newly acquired vocabulary and tell sentences to each other.

Grammar: Possessive Pronouns

Write the possessive pronoun from the box that takes the place of the words in dark print.

His	Their

1. The divers' robot helped them. _____

2. The teacher's book is missing. _____

3. The players' uniforms are blue. _____

4. The boy's bike is outside. _____

Circle the pronoun that completes each sentence. Write the pronoun on the line. Say the sentence.

5. The children found _____ toys.

    his   their

6. My brother wore _____ jacket.

    his   their

7. Angela saw _____ friend at the park.

    her   their

8. They ride _____ bikes to school.

    his   their

Beginning/Intermediate Read the directions for each section and model examples 1 and 5. Have children work with partners to write the right pronoun. Have them say sentences 5–8 to each other.

Name _____

Read each question and prompt. Discuss the answers with your group. Use _Meet the Super Croc_ to find details to support your answers. Then write your answers on the blank lines or on another sheet of paper.

1. Summarize _Meet the Super Croc_ using a few sentences.

   _____

2. How large is the giant crocodile discussed in the story?

   _____

3. Discuss the similarities and differences between the giant croc, the Australian crocodile and the American alligator.

   _____

4. Why did Sereno make copies of the bones?

   _____

5. Share ideas on what you like and dislike about the job of Paul Sereno.

   _____

6. Write one question about _Meet the Super Croc_ to ask your group.

   _____

   _____

Beginning/Intermediate Read the directions. Pair children to answer the questions using basic and content vocabulary. Have them share answers with the group. If needed, they can listen to the selection on **StudentsWork Plus Online**.

Name _____

Phonics/Word Study: Words with Consonant + -*le* Syllables

Draw a line to break each word into syllables.
Then match the word to the picture it names.

1. apple

2. saddle

3. turtle

4. puzzle

5. candle

6. marble

7. needle

8. beetle

Beginning/Intermediate Review how to decode words. Read and point to the first word with the consonant + -*le* syllable. Point out your mouth position. Have children say the words and listen to the **Sound Pronunciation CD**.

Name_____

Phonics: Words with Consonant and *-le* Syllables

Divide each word into syllables. Write the word parts on the lines.

Example: noodle _____noo_____ _____dle_____

1. middle _____ _____

2. little _____ _____

3. wiggle _____ _____

4. dimple _____ _____

5. bundle _____ _____

6. riddle _____ _____

7. circle _____ _____

8. sample _____ _____

Read the Decodable Reader *Puddle Pet* with a partner.

Beginning/Intermediate Read the directions and model the example.
Have children complete the page with a partner and say the words to
each other.

Use the word chart to study this week's vocabulary words. Write a sentence using each word in your writer's notebook.

Word	Context Sentence	Illustration
giggled _____	Kim and Rosa giggled at the playful puppy.	**Name something that makes you giggle.**
fluttered _____	A butterfly fluttered from flower to flower.	
peered _____	The cat peered from under the bed.	
recognized _____	I cannot recognize the person in the mask.	
vanished _____	The seal slipped into the ocean and vanished.	
snuggled _____	The baby ducks snuggled together next to their mother.	**What animals have you seen snuggled together?**

© Macmillan/McGraw-Hill

Beginning/Intermediate Review vocabulary. Use gestures to demonstrate meaning. Pair children to write sentences, or draw pictures, to illustrate the meaning of the newly acquired vocabulary and tell sentences to each other.

Grammar: Contractions
Write the contractions for the underlined words.
Write the new sentence on the line below. Say the sentence.

1. <u>We are</u> at the animal shelter. _____

   _____.

2. <u>It is</u> on South Street. _____

   _____.

3. <u>We are</u> going to get a kitten. _____

   _____.

4. <u>It is</u> hard to pick just one kitten. _____

   _____.

5. <u>They are</u> all very cute. _____

   _____.

6. Mom says <u>she is</u> ready to pick one. _____

   _____.

7. <u>It is</u> a white male kitten. _____

   _____.

8. <u>He is</u> going to be a big cat. _____

   _____.

Beginning/Intermediate Read the directions. Review contractions.
Model when to use them. Have children work with a partner to write the
contractions. Then have them read the new sentence to each other.

Grade 2 Unit 5 Week 4 119

Name_____

Read each question and prompt. Discuss the answers with your group. Use *Farfallina and Marcel* to find details to support your answers. Then write your answers on the blank lines or on another sheet of paper.

1. Explain how you know that *Farfallina and Marcel* is a fantasy story.

   _____

2. Farfallina hides close to the ground and Marcel hides behind the tree. Tell why they do this.

   _____

3. What did you think happened to Farfallina when she decided to climb up the tree?

   _____

4. What real information is in this fantasy story? Tell three things you learned.

   _____

5. Tell the group about the illustration you like best. Tell why you like it.

   _____

6. Write one question about *Farfallina and Marcel* to ask your group.

   _____

Beginning/Intermediate Read the directions. Pair children to answer the questions using basic and content vocabulary. Have them share answers with the group. If needed, they can listen to the selection on **StudentsWork Plus Online.**

© Macmillan/McGraw-Hill

Name_____

Phonics/Word Study: Words with Open Syllables

Put the two syllables together. Write the word on the line. Say the word.

1. ro   bot   _____

2. e   qual   _____

3. fa   vor   _____

4. gra   vy   _____

5. la   dy   _____

Write the word from the list that matches the picture.

6.    _____

7.    _____

Beginning/Intermediate Review how to decode words. Read and point to two words with open syllables. Point out your mouth position. Have children say the words and listen to the **Sound Pronunciation CD**.

Grade 2 Unit 5 Week 5   121

Phonics: Words with Open Syllables
Divide each word into syllables. Write the word parts on the lines.

1. motor   _____   _____

2. secret   _____   _____

3. crazy   _____   _____

4. navy   _____   _____

5. frozen   _____   _____

6. human   _____   _____

7. hotel   _____   _____

8. bonus   _____   _____

Read the Decodable Reader *Doggy Door* with a partner.

Beginning/Intermediate Read the directions and model example 1. Have children complete the page with a partner and say the words to each other.

Name_____

Use the word chart to study this week's vocabulary words.
Write a sentence using each word in your writer's notebook.

Word	Context Sentence	Illustration
beloved _____	I hug my <u>beloved</u> grandfather.	
promised _____	We <u>promised</u> that we'd be friends forever.	
wiggled _____	I <u>wiggled</u> into last year's shirt.	
gleamed _____	The ice <u>gleamed</u> in the bright sun.	**Name something else that gleams in the sun.**
glanced _____	I <u>glanced</u> quickly at the dog as I walked past.	
noble _____	The queen looked <u>noble</u> as she sat on the throne.	

© Macmillan/McGraw-Hill

Beginning/Intermediate Review vocabulary. Ask children to identify Spanish cognates. Pair children to write sentences, or draw pictures, to illustrate the meaning of the newly acquired vocabulary and tell sentences to each other.

Grade 2 Unit 5 Week 5 123

Name _____

Grammar: Pronoun/Verb Agreement

Underline the verb that agrees with the pronoun in each sentence.

1. They (plants, plant) tomatoes in their garden.

2. She (carve, carves) the pumpkin.

3. I (eat, eats) pumpkin pie for desert.

4. He (washes, wash) the dishes.

Circle the pronoun that agrees with the verb.
Write the pronoun on the line. Say the sentence.

5. _____ buy seeds at the store.

   She   We

6. _____ works in the garden.

   They   He

7. _____ grows pumpkins every year.

   She   They

8. _____ grow very big.

   He   They

Beginning/Intermediate Read the directions for each section and model the first example. Have children work with partners to complete the page. Have them share their sentences with the group.

Name_____

Read each question and prompt. Discuss the answers with your group. Use *Nutik, the Wolf Pup* to find details to support your answers. Then write your answers on the blank lines or on another sheet of paper.

1. Describe Amaroq's family. How do they feel about him? Support your answer with examples.

   _____

2. Amaroq tells his sister he will not fall in love with Nutik. Do you think he can keep his promise?

   _____

3. Tell what you learned about life in an Eskimo village.

   _____

4. Talk about things in the story that are not real.

   _____

5. Describe the most exciting event in the story. How did it make you feel?

   _____

6. Write one question about *Nutik, the Wolf Pup* to ask your group.

   _____

   _____

Phonics/Word Study: Words with Consonant and *-le* Syllables

Put the two syllables together. Write the word. Say the word. Then match the word to the picture it names.

1. bot   tle   _____

2. puz   zle   _____

3. rat   tle   _____

4. bee   tle   _____

5. jun   gle   _____

6. whis   tle   _____

7. fid   dle   _____

8. cat   tle   _____

Beginning/Intermediate Review how to decode words. Read and point to the first word with the consonant + -le syllable. Point out your mouth position. Have children say the words and listen to the **Sound Pronunciation CD**.

Name_____

Phonics: Words with Consonant and -*le* Syllables
Divide each word into syllables. Write the word parts on the lines.

1. maple   _____   _____

2. cuddle   _____   _____

3. crumble   _____   _____

4. simple   _____   _____

5. purple   _____   _____

6. doodle   _____   _____

7. fizzle   _____   _____

Read the Decodable Reader *The Camping Trip* with a partner.

© Macmillan/McGraw-Hill

Beginning/Intermediate Read the directions and model example 1. Have children complete the page with a partner and say the words to each other.

Name_____

Use the word chart to study this week's vocabulary words.
Write a sentence using each word in your writer's notebook.

Word	Context Sentence	Illustration
burrow _____	I saw a rabbit run into its <u>burrow</u> and hide.	**Which animal lives in a burrow—an eagle or a gopher?**
beyond _____	We are not allowed to go <u>beyond</u> the fence.	
warning _____	When a cat hisses, it is a <u>warning</u> sign to leave it alone.	
lengthy _____	There was a <u>lengthy</u> wait to get into the park.	**If a wait is lengthy, is it long or short?**
distant _____	I can see the <u>distant</u> stars.	

© Macmillan/McGraw-Hill

Beginning/Intermediate Review vocabulary. Use gestures to demonstrate meaning. Pair children to write sentences, or draw pictures, to illustrate the meaning of the newly acquired vocabulary and tell sentences to each other.

Name _____

Grammar: Adjectives
Underline the adjective in each sentence.
Say the sentence.

1. Sofia had a good plan.

2. Sofia bought purple ribbons.

3. She made a nice mobile.

4. It was a special gift.

Write an adjective from the box to complete
each sentence. Use each word only once.

young	beautiful	silver

5. Sofia bought _____ bells.

6. Sofia had a _____ sister.

7. She gave her a _____ mobile.

Beginning/Intermediate Read the directions. Review adjectives.
Ask children to brainstorm some examples. Have children work with a
partner to complete the page, then read the sentences to each other.

Grade 2 Unit 6 Week 1 129

Read each question and prompt. Discuss the answers with your group. Use *Dig, Wait, Listen: A Desert Toad's Tale* to find details to support your answers. Then write your answers on the blank lines or on another sheet of paper.

1. Tell what the author of *Dig, Wait, Listen: A Desert Toad's Tale* wants to share with this story.

   _____

2. Name the animals that share the desert with the spadefood toad.

   _____

3. Tell why you think the woodpecker is tapping on the cactus.

   _____

4. The toad's eggs hatch very fast. Why is this important?

   _____

5. Share ideas about what the young toads will do when they leap into the desert.

   _____

6. Write one question about *Dig, Wait, Listen: A Desert Toad's Tale* to ask your group.

   _____

   _____

Beginning/Intermediate Read the directions. Pair children to answer the questions using basic and content vocabulary. Have them share answers with the group. If needed, they can listen to the selection on **StudentsWork Plus Online**.

Phonics/Word Study: Vowel Team Syllables
Put the two syllables together. Write the word. Say the word. Then match the word to the picture it names.

1. bee   tle   _____

2. thir   teen   _____

3. mon   key   _____

4. rain   coat   _____

5. bird   house   _____

6. rac   coon   _____

7. cray   on   _____

8. paint   brush   _____

Beginning/Intermediate Review how to decode words. Read and point to the first three words with vowel team syllables. Point out your mouth position. Have children say the words and listen to the **Sound Pronunciation CD**.

Phonics: Vowel Team Syllables

Read the words in the word box. Write the words with the same vowel team next to the letters.

sixteen	roadmap	noisy	away
enjoy	poison	midweek	approach
toy	rainbow	around	ready
Sunday	remain	discount	weather

Example:

ee   <u>sixteen</u>   <u>midweek</u>

ai   _____   _____

ay   _____   _____

ea   _____   _____

oa   _____   _____

oi   _____   _____

oy   _____   _____

ou   _____   _____

Read the Decodable Reader *The Turtle* with a partner.

Beginning/Intermediate Read the directions. Then read the words in the box and have children repeat. Have partners complete the page.

Name _____

Use the word chart to study this week's vocabulary words.
Write a sentence using each word in your writer's notebook.

Word	Context Sentence	Illustration
beasts _____	We saw many different <u>beasts</u> at the zoo.	How are the words beasts and animals the same? How are they different?
puddles _____	The fox lapped water from the <u>puddle</u>.	
nibble _____	The mouse <u>nibbles</u> on a big piece of cheese.	Give examples of things you might nibble on.
itches _____	I have <u>itches</u> all over from bug bites.	
preen _____	My cats like to <u>preen</u> each other.	
handy _____	A step stool is a <u>handy</u> tool.	

© Macmillan/McGraw-Hill

Beginning/Intermediate Review vocabulary. Use gestures to demonstrate meaning.
Pair children to write sentences, or draw pictures, to illustrate the meaning of the newly
acquired vocabulary and tell sentences to each other.